Thank you...

... for purchasing this copy of Telling the Time Book 1. We hope that you find our materials helpful as part of your programme of numeracy activities.

Please note that photocopies can only be made for use by the purchasing institution. Supplying copies to other schools, institutions or individuals breaches the copyright licence. Thank you for your help in this.

This Telling the Time book is part of our growing range of educational titles. Most of our books are individual workbooks but, due to popular demand, we are now introducing a greater number of photocopiable titles especially for teachers.

You may like to look out for:

TELLING THE TIME BOOK 2

TIMES TABLES RESOURCE BOOK

READING FOR LITERACY *for ages 5–7, 7–8, 8–9, 9–10, 10–11*

WRITING FOR LITERACY *for ages 5–7, 7–8, 8–9, 9–10, 10–11*

SPELLING FOR LITERACY *for ages 5–7, 7–8, 8–9, 9–10, 10–11*

NUMERACY TODAY *for ages 5–7, 7–9, 9–11*

HOMEWORK TODAY *for ages 5–7, 7–8, 8–9, 9–10, 10–11*

BEST HANDWRITING *for ages 4–7, 7–11*

WET PLAY TODAY FOR AGES 5–7, 7–9, 9–11

To find details of our other publications, please visit our website: **www.acblack.com**

Telling the time at Key Stage 1

Pupils need to learn how to tell the time using both analogue and digital clocks. Pupils in Year 1 are expected to learn how to tell the time to the hour or half-hour using an analogue clock. In Year 2 this is extended to quarter hours, using both analogue and digital clocks.

'Telling' the time extends beyond the simple reading of times from clocks.

Pupils in Year 1 need to develop an understanding of the following:

- days and weeks

- seasons

- months

- times of the day such as morning, afternoon and evening

- other time vocabulary such as today, tomorrow, yesterday and weekend.

Pupils in Year 2 need to extend this understanding to include:

- names of months

- vocabulary such as minute, second and fortnight

- relationships between times: knowing that one week is 7 days, one day is 24 hours, one hour is 60 minutes and one minute is 60 seconds.

Telling the time at Key Stage 2

Pupils extend their knowledge of how to tell the time using both analogue and digital clocks. Pupils in Year 3 are expected to learn how to tell the time to five minutes on analogue and digital clocks. In Year 4 this is extended to reading time to exact minutes on analogue clocks and 12-hour digital clocks. In Year 5 pupils should be able to read time to exact minutes on 24-hour digital clocks.

Pupils in Year 3 need to develop an understanding of the following:

 centuries

 calendars and dates

 a.m. and p.m.

 relationships between times, e.g. knowing that one year is 365 days or 52 weeks or 12 months.

Pupils in Year 4 need to extend their use of the calendar and begin to study the use of timetables. They learn about leap years and begin to know how many days are in each month.

Work with timetables is developed further in Year 5.

In Year 6, pupils learn to use world time charts as well as learning about Greenwich Mean Time and British Summer Time. In both Key Stages pupils are encouraged to make estimates of time spans.

In this book we concentrate particularly on the processes of 'telling' the time using analogue clocks, digital clocks, and calendars. As an extension to this work you may like to use our companion title, Telling the Time Book 2.

Contents

Contents

© Andrew Brodie Publications   www.acblack.com

OHP/Display: The face of a clock

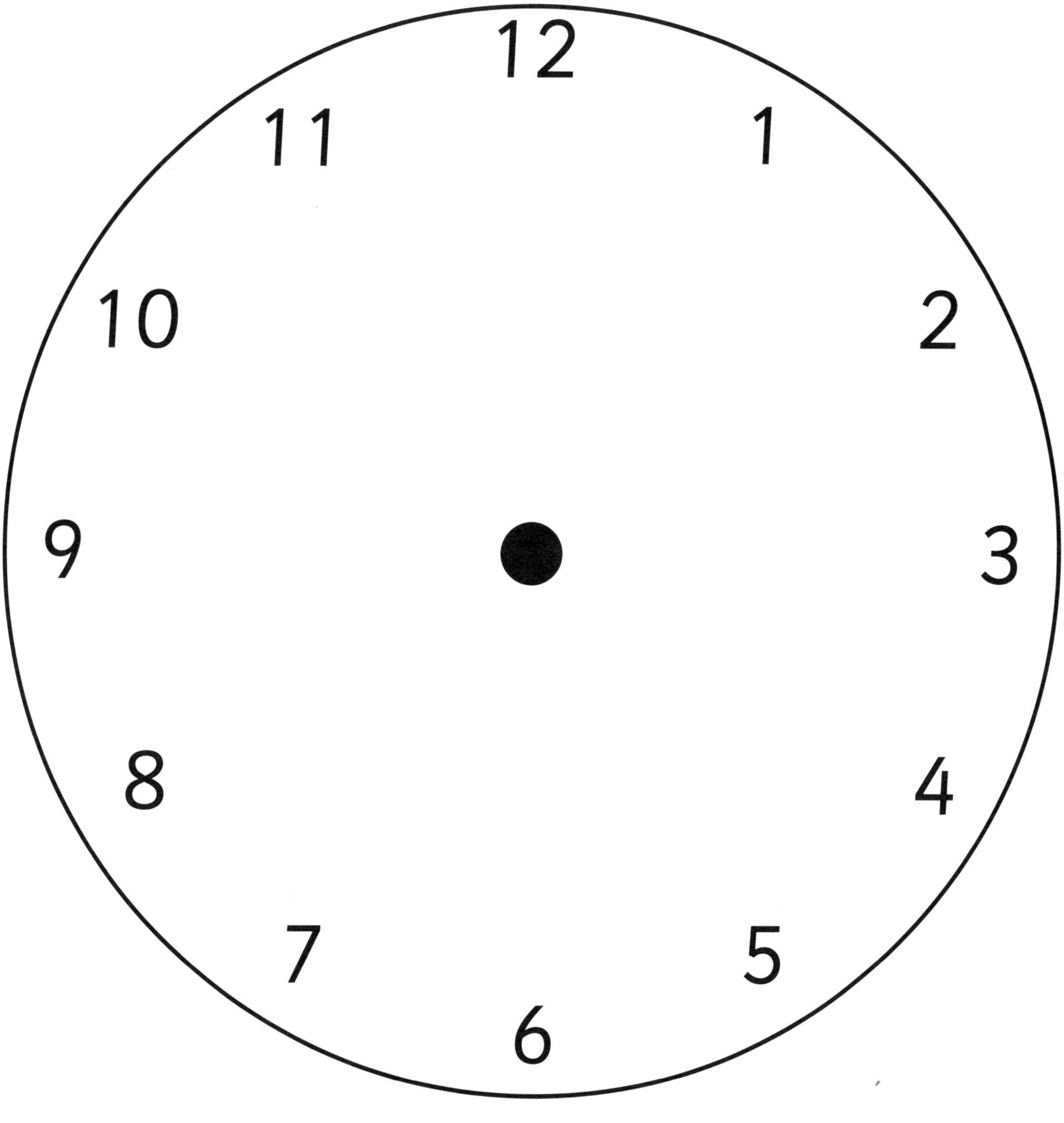
12
11
1
10
2
9
3
8
4
7
5
6

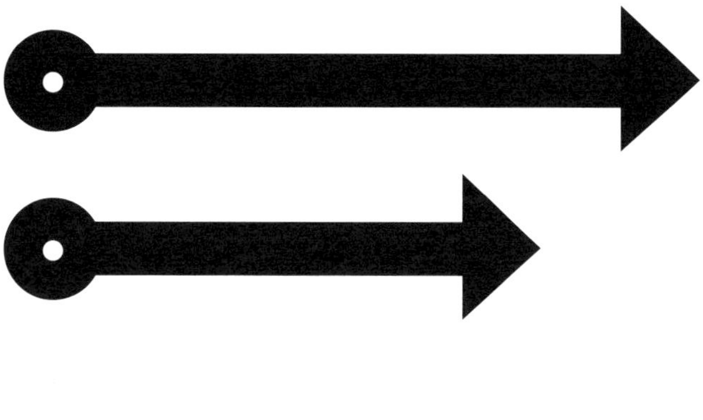

Name:

Worksheet: The clock face

Draw hands on the clock.

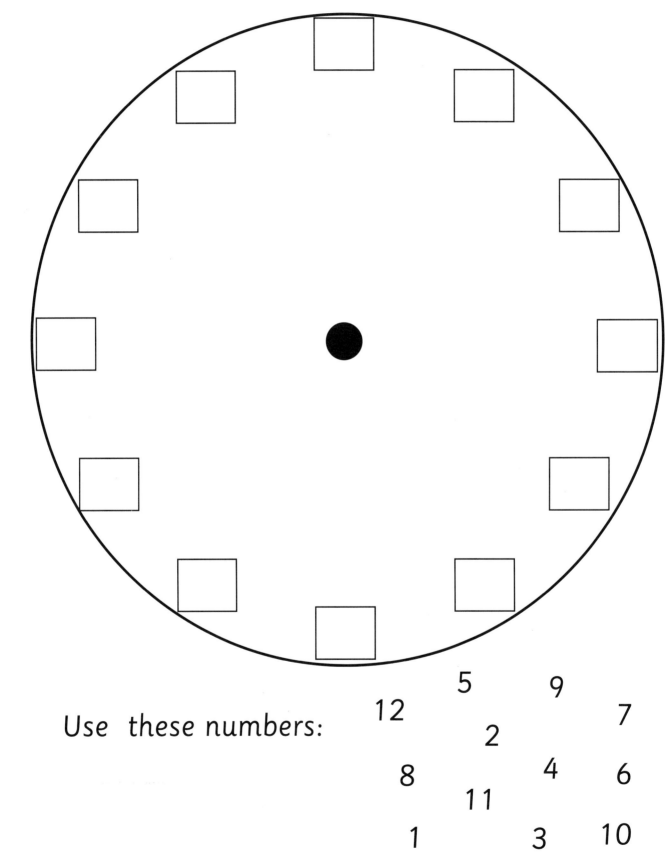

Use these numbers:

12   5   9   7

2

8   4   6

11

1   3   10

Clock faces

Write the times shown on these clocks.

9 o'clock		

Write the times shown on these clocks.

| 1 o'clock | | |

Write the times shown on these clocks.

| half past 4 | | |

| | | |

Write the times shown on these clocks.

| half past 7 | | |

| | | |

Monday

Tuesday

Wednesday

Thursday

Friday

Saturday

Sunday

Days: Wednesday   Sunday   Tuesday
      Friday   Thursday   Monday   Saturday

Write the days in order.
Draw ☺ for your favourite days.

Today is _____

Fill in the gap.

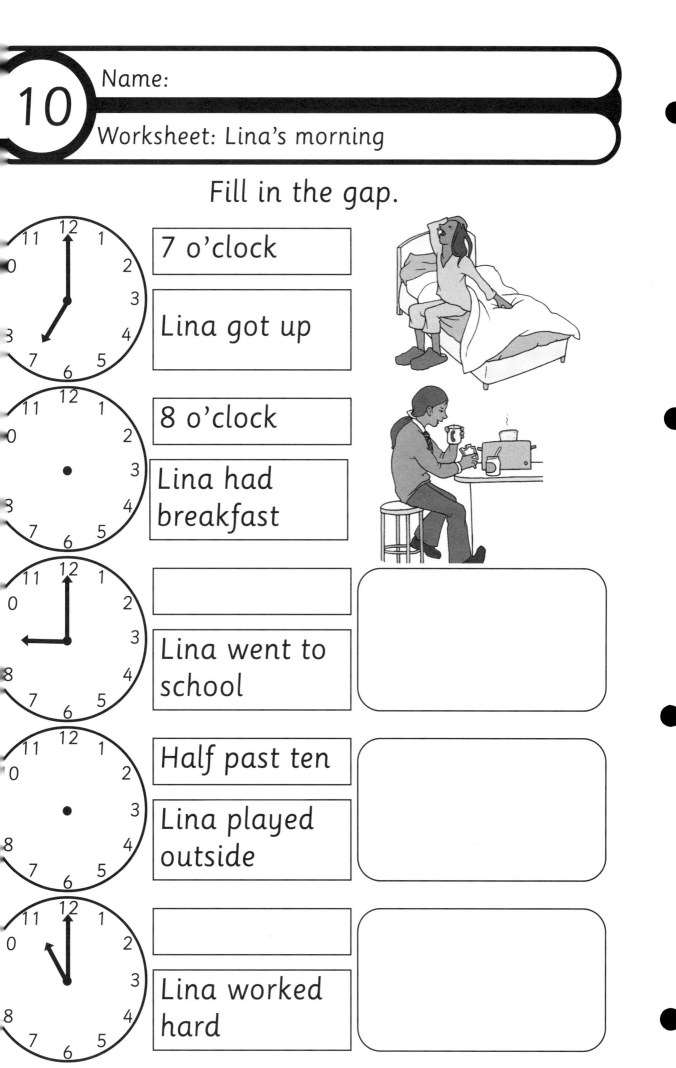

Clock	Text
	7 o'clock
	Lina got up
	8 o'clock
	Lina had breakfast
	Lina went to school
	Half past ten
	Lina played outside
	Lina worked hard

Andrew Brodie Publications   www.acblack.com

Fill in the boxes to show your morning.

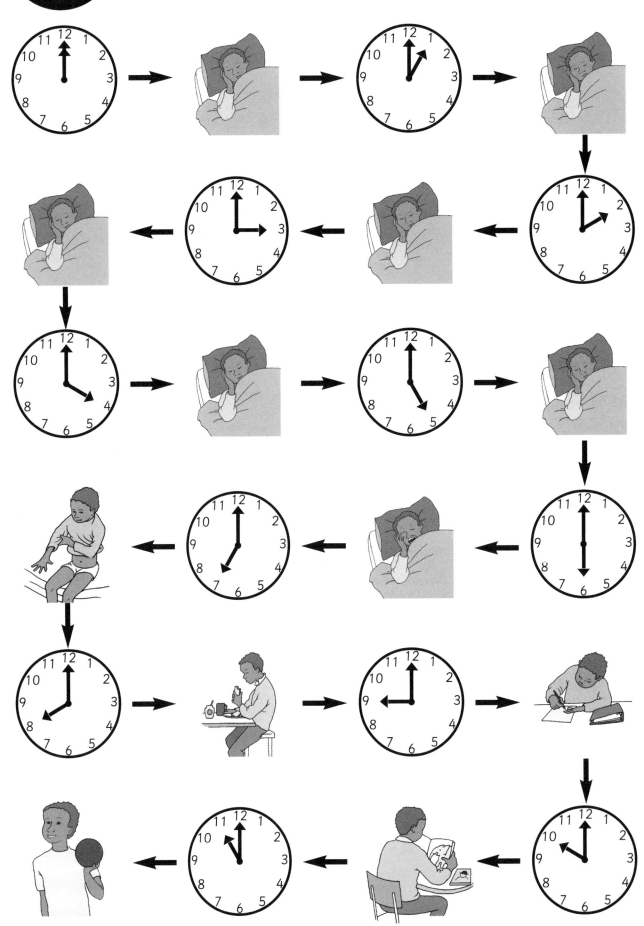

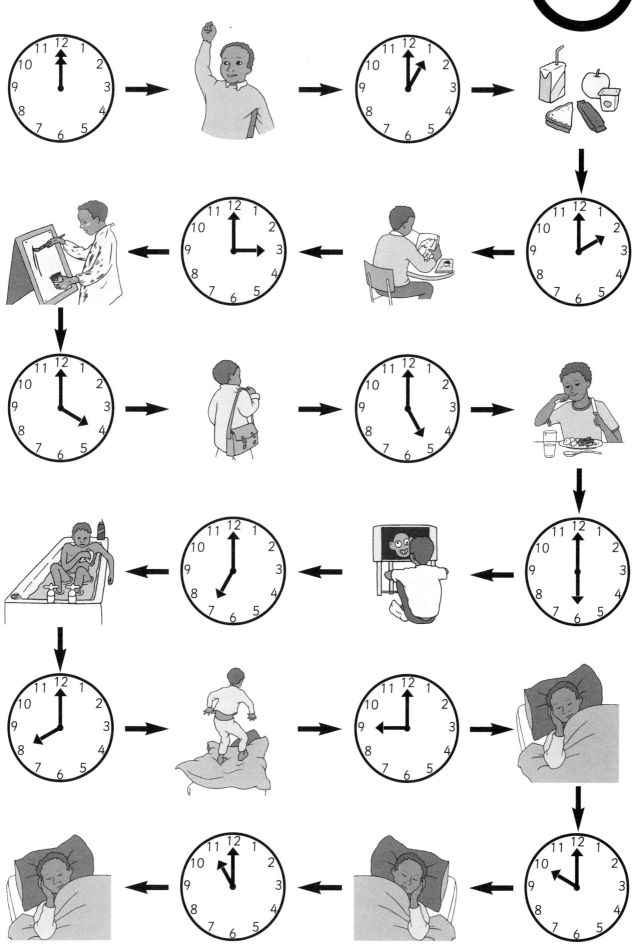

January

February

March

April

May

June

July

August

September

October

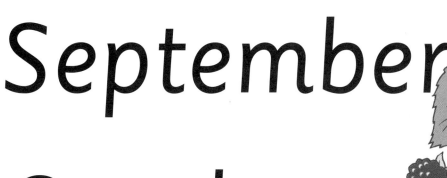

November

December

Fill in the missing months.
You will need to turn the paper around to write the words.
Draw a picture for each season.

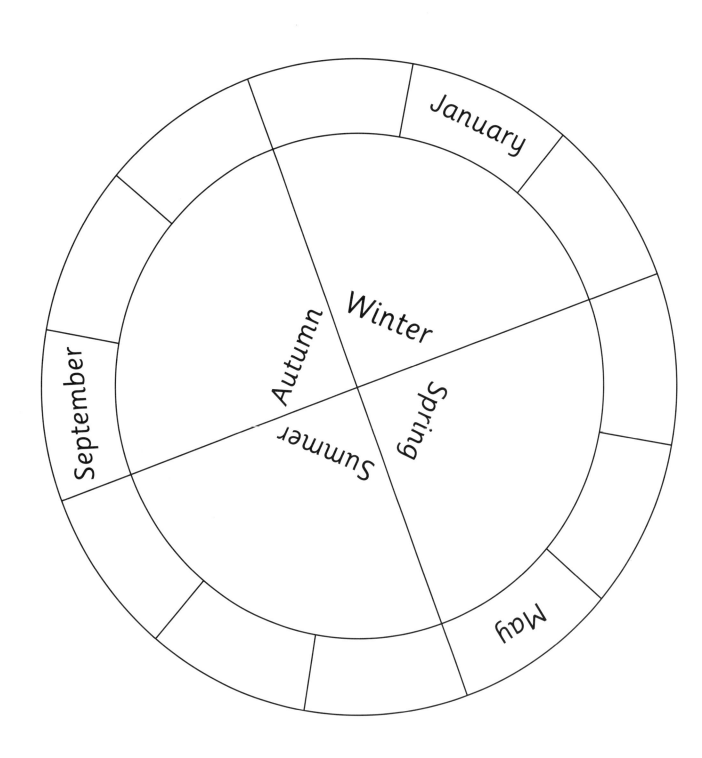

Here are the months of the year:

May	January	October	April
December	March	September	June
February	August	November	July

Write the months in order.

Which month is it now?

In which month
is your birthday?

Name:

Worksheet: Write the time (1)

Write the times shown on these clocks.

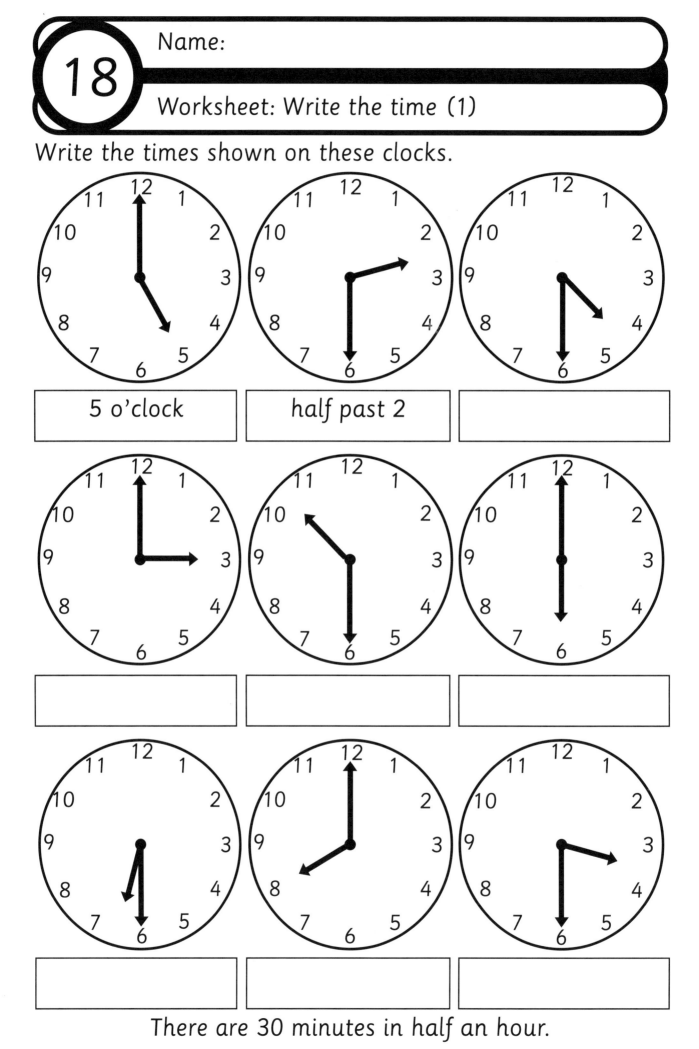

5 o'clock

half past 2

There are 30 minutes in half an hour.

Write the times shown on these clocks.

half past 8	7 o'clock	

How many minutes are there in half an hour?

This clock shows 15 minutes past 5 o'clock.
We can write:

15 minutes past 5

or

quarter past 5.

Write the times in two ways.

Name:

Worksheet: Quarter past (2)

Write the times in two ways.

| 15 minutes past 10 | | |
| quarter past 10 | | |

Name:

Worksheet: Quarter to (1)

This clock shows 15 minutes to 5 o'clock.

We can write:

15 minutes to 5

or

quarter to 5.

Write the times in two ways.

Write the times in two ways.

15 minutes to 1	

quarter to 1	

Look at how numbers are formed on digital clocks. Each digit can be made by using combinations of long thin bars.

Each of these bars has six sides so they are long thin _ _ _ _ _ _ _ _ .

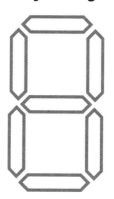

Look at the numbers:

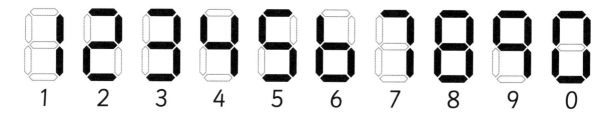

1   2   3   4   5   6   7   8   9   0

Colour the bars to show these times.

6 o'clock   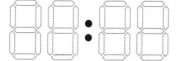   10 o'clock   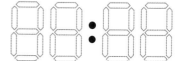

12 o'clock   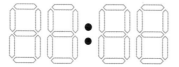   4 o'clock   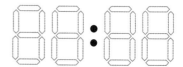

7 o'clock   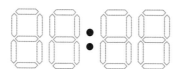   3 o'clock   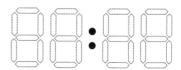

11 o'clock   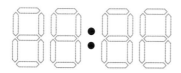   12 o'clock   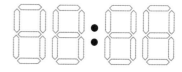

This analogue clock shows 4 o'clock.

This digital clock shows 4 o'clock.

Match these analogue clocks to the digital clocks and fill in the blanks.

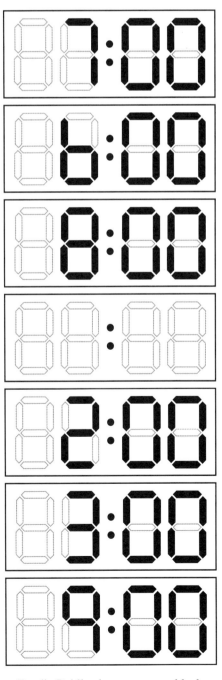

Name:

Worksheet: Digital figures (2)

Look at how we can make numbers by colouring in the bars on a digital display:

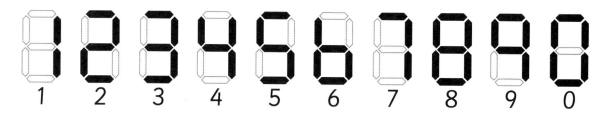

1   2   3   4   5   6   7   8   9   0

This clock shows half past 7:

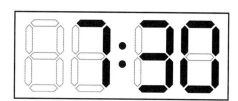

Colour the bars to show these times.

half past 5 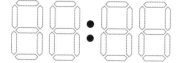   half past 9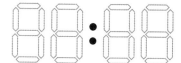

half past 1 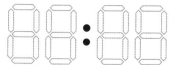   half past 3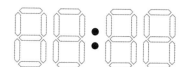

half past 12 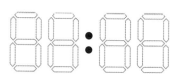   half past 2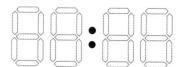

half past 8 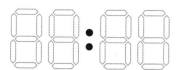   half past 6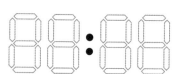

What times do these clocks show?

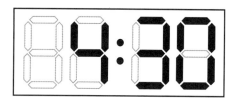   

This analogue clock shows
half past five ...

... so does this
digital clock.

Match these analogue clocks to the digital
clocks and fill in the blanks.

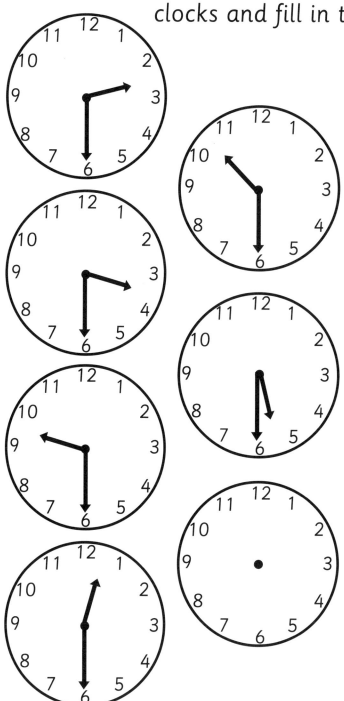

Look at how we can make numbers by colouring in the bars on a digital display:

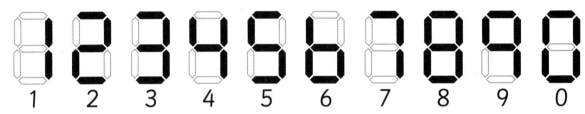

1   2   3   4   5   6   7   8   9   0

This clock shows quarter past 4: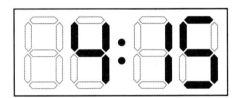

Colour the bars to show these times.

quarter past 7 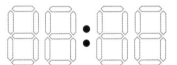 quarter past 10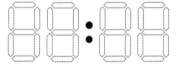

quarter past 12 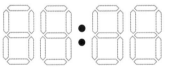 quarter past 3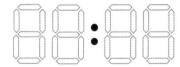

quarter past 9 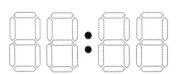 quarter past 1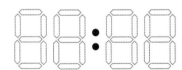

quarter past 8 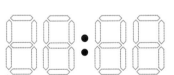 quarter past 11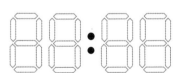

What times do these clocks show?

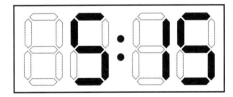

This analogue clock shows quarter past seven ...

... so does this digital clock.

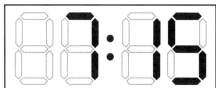

Match these analogue clocks to the digital clocks and fill in the blanks.

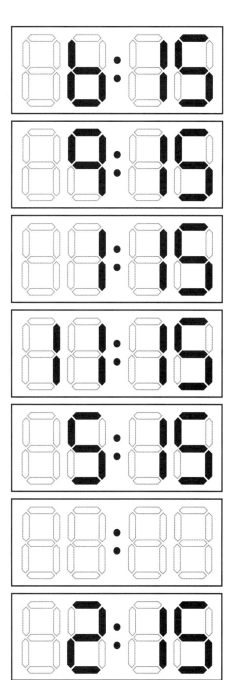

Look at how we can make numbers by colouring in the bars on a digital display:

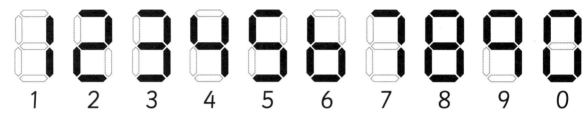

1   2   3   4   5   6   7   8   9   0

This clock shows quarter to 4. Remember, the last o'clock time before quarter to 4 must have been 3 o'clock.

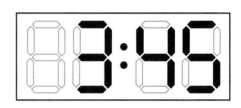

Colour the bars to show these times.

quarter past 7

quarter past 10

quarter past 12

quarter past 3

quarter past 9

quarter past 1

quarter past 8

quarter past 11

What times do these clocks show?

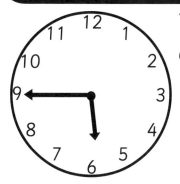 This analogue clock shows quarter to six ...

... so does this digital clock.

Look. It says 5 because the last o'clock time was 5 o'clock but it still shows 15 minutes <u>to</u> 6.

Match these analogue clocks to the digital clocks and fill in the blanks.

What times do these clocks show?
Write: ...... o'clock, or half past ...... or quarter past ......
or quarter to ......

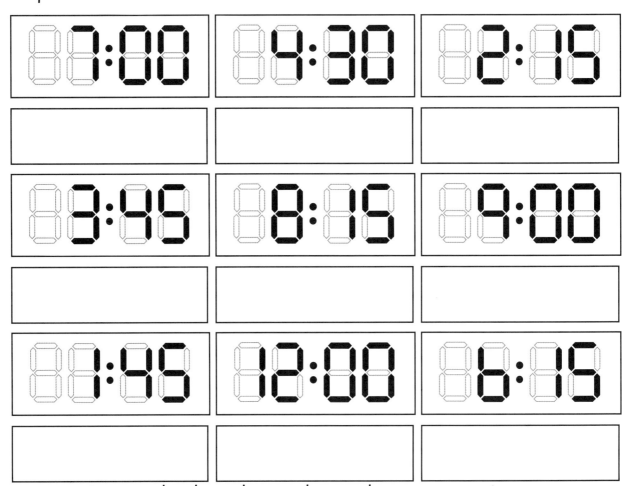

Draw the hands to show the correct times.

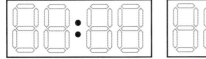 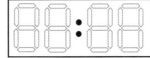 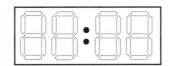 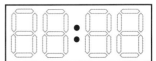

5 o'clock   quarter past 5   half past 5   quarter to 6

Colour the bars to show the same times.

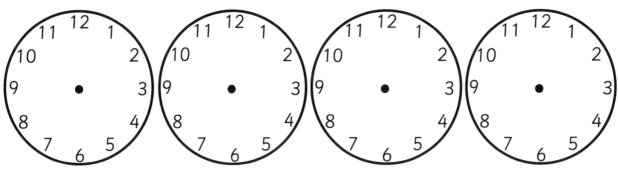

Here is part of a calendar, showing June 2005.

M	T	W	T	F	S	S
		1	2	3	4	5
6	7	8	9	10	11	12
13	14	15	16	17	18	19
20	21	22	23	24	25	26
27	28	29	30			

Here are three ways in which we can write a date:

2nd June 2005   02.06.05   2/6/05

↑   ↑

We write 6 because June is the sixth month in the year.

Write each of these dates in two other ways.

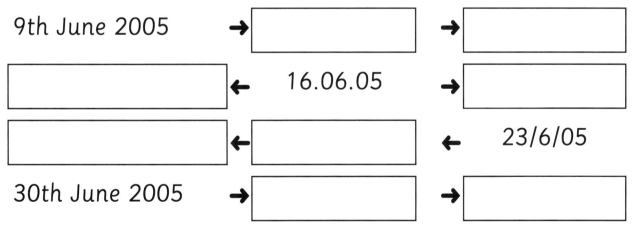

9th June 2005   → [   ]   → [   ]

[   ] ← 16.06.05   → [   ]

[   ] ← [   ]   ← 23/6/05

30th June 2005   → [   ]   → [   ]

Draw a ring around each of these dates on the calendar above. What day of the week do they all show?

[   ]

On the back of this sheet show the calendar for this month.

Here is part of a calendar, showing March 2006.

M	T	W	T	F	S	S
		1	2	3	4	5
6	7	8	9	10	11	12
13	14	15	16	17	18	19
20	21	22	23	24	25	26
27	28	29	30	31		

What day of the week is 1/3/06?

How many days are there in March?

What day of the week is 31/3/06?

How many Mondays are there in March 2006?

How many Tuesdays are there in March 2006?

How many Wednesdays are there in March 2006?

How many Thursdays are there in March 2006?

How many Fridays are there in March 2006?

How many Saturdays are there in March 2006?

How many Sundays are there in March 2006?

What day of the week is 28th February 2006?

What day of the week is 1st April 2006?

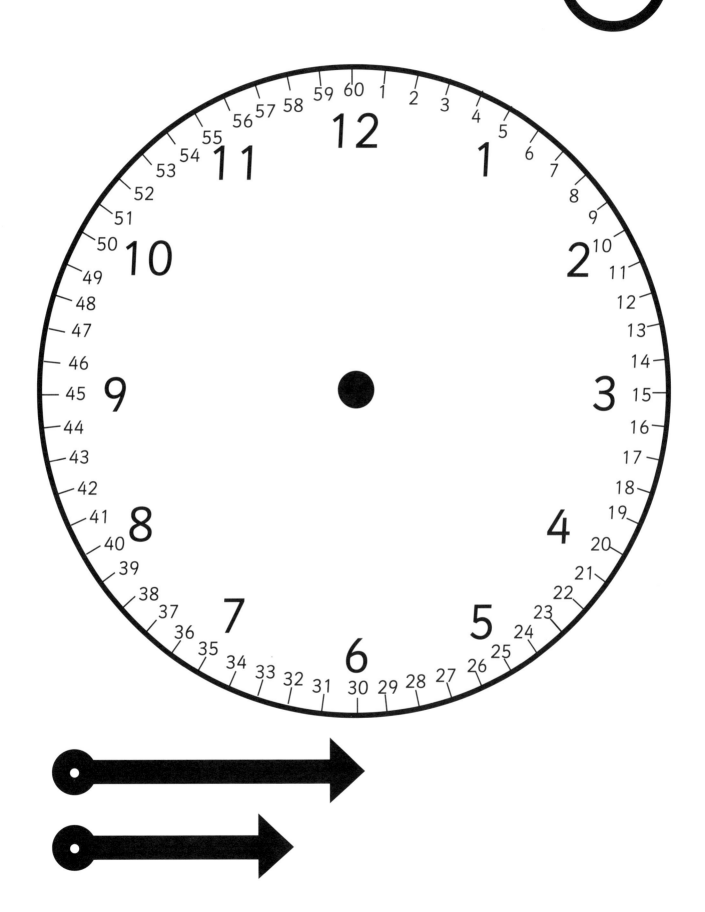

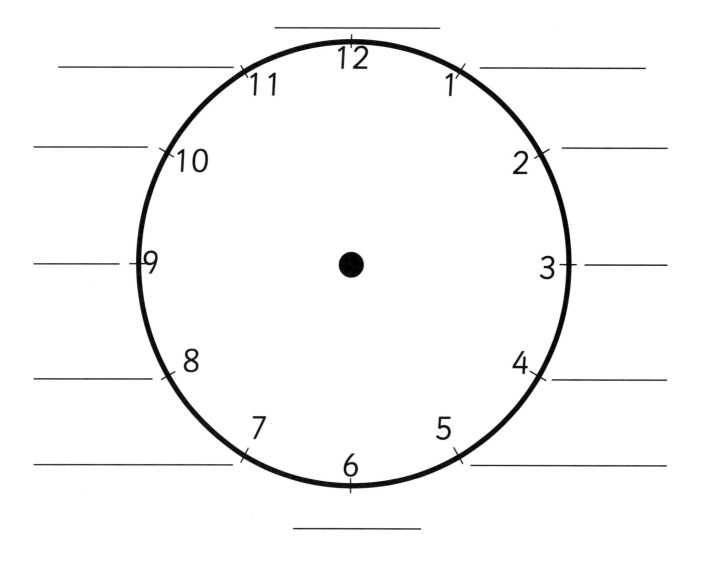

Name:

Worksheet: Label the clock

Word Bank

five minutes past   ten minutes past

ten minutes to   half past   twenty minutes past

twenty minutes to   twenty-five minutes past

five minutes to   quarter to

quarter past   twenty-five minutes to

We can write this time like this:
five minutes past 6 o'clock
But we usually shorten it to
five past 6.

five past 6

Write the times shown on these clocks.

We can write this time like this:
five minutes to 6 o'clock
But we usually shorten it to:
five to 6.

five to 6

Write the times shown on these clocks.

This analogue clock shows ten past five.

This digital clock shows ten past five.

5:10

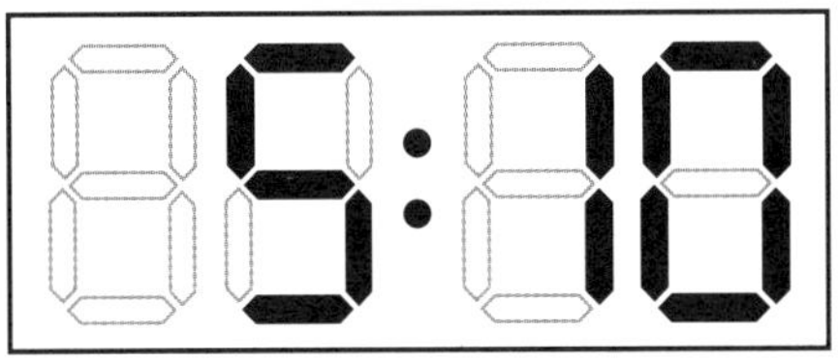

Draw the hands or colour the bars to make these pairs of clocks match. Write the times.

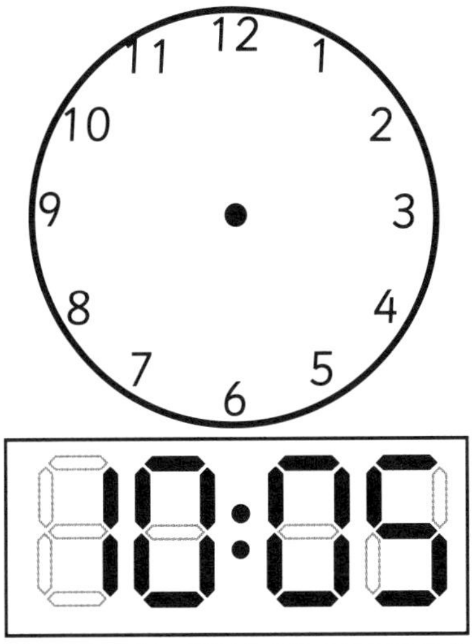

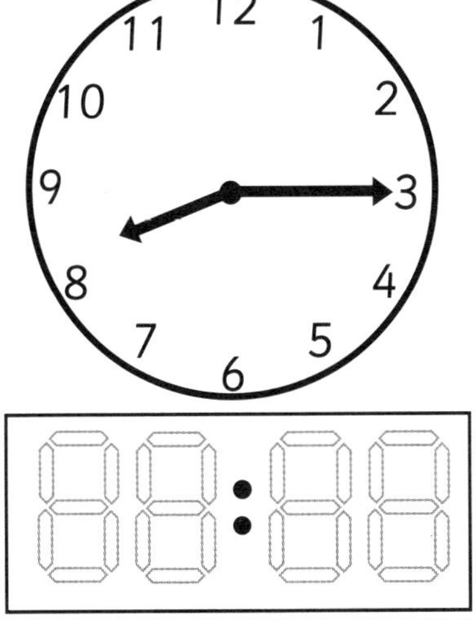

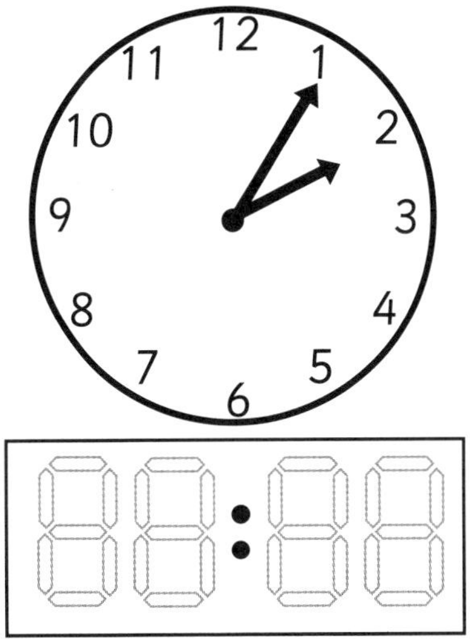

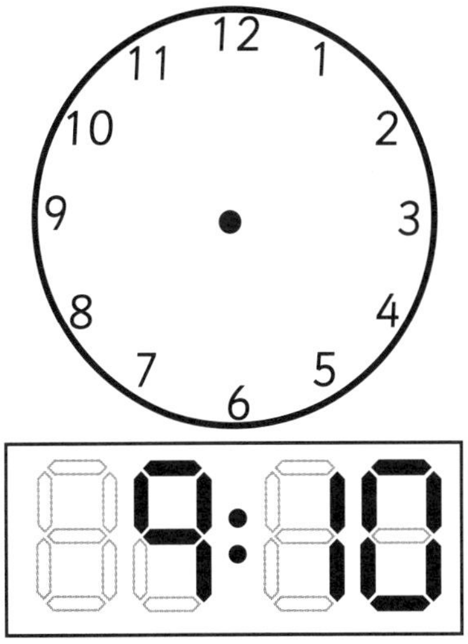

10:05

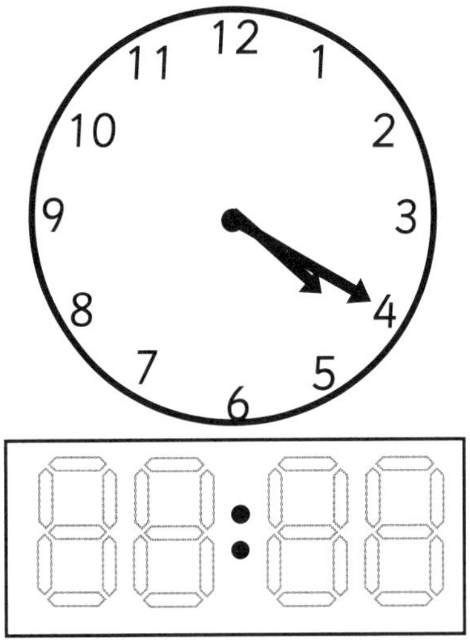

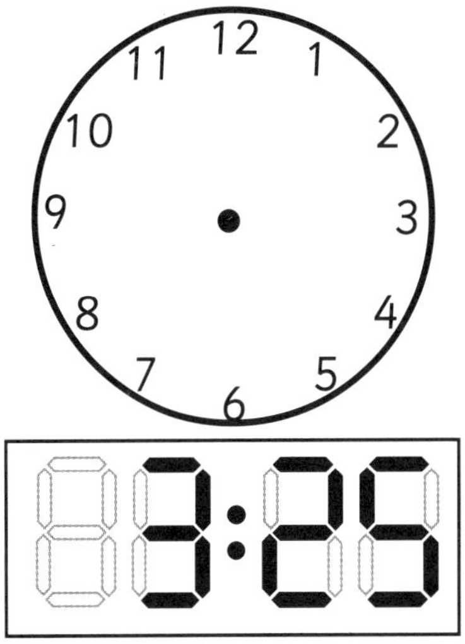

88:88

3:25

88:88

88:88

9:10

Draw the hands or colour the bars to make these pairs of clocks match.
Write the times.

Name:

Worksheet: Blank analogues and digitals

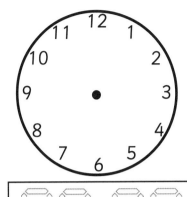
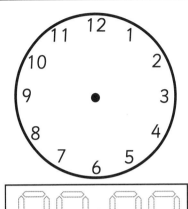
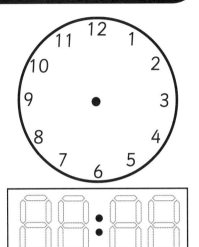

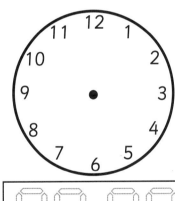
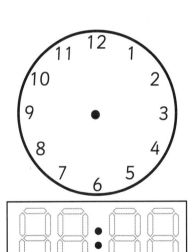

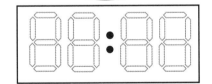
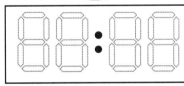

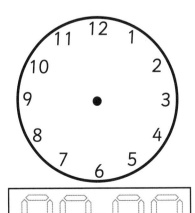
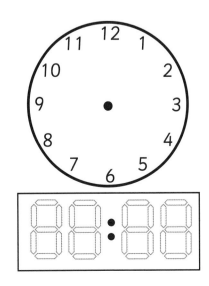
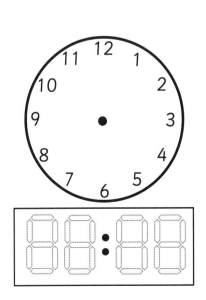

Name:

Worksheet: a.m. and p.m. times

The time shown on this clock is 9.35.
If it is 9.35 in the morning we would write 9.35 <u>a.m.</u>
If it is 9.35 in the evening we would write 9.35 <u>p.m.</u>
All times before 12 o'clock noon are written as a.m. times.
All times after 12 o'clock noon are written as p.m. times.

afternoon

morning

afternoon

morning

afternoon

evening

afternoon

morning

morning

afternoon

evening

afternoon

Match the times.
We've done the first
one for you.

1 day	60 seconds
1 minute	12 months
1 week	24 hours
1 year	60 minutes
1 fortnight	7 days
1 hour	100 years
1 century	2 weeks

We live in the 21st century.
Your parents were born in the 20th century.
The 20th century began at the start of the year 1900
and ended at the end of 1999.

Match the centuries.
We've done one for you.

The 20th century	1700 – 1799
The 15th century	1000 – 1099
The 18th century	1600 – 1699
The 11th century	1900 – 1999
The 17th century	1400 – 1499
The 19th century	1800 – 1899

Name:

Worksheet: Minutes past the hour

Fill in the missing times.

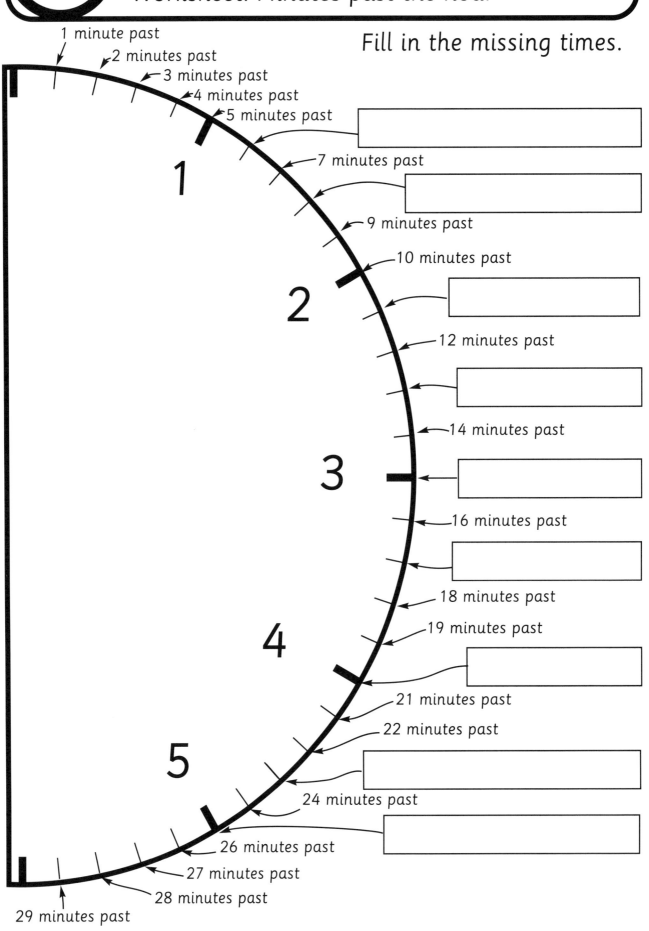

1 minute past

2 minutes past

3 minutes past

4 minutes past

5 minutes past

1

7 minutes past

9 minutes past

10 minutes past

2

12 minutes past

14 minutes past

3

16 minutes past

18 minutes past

19 minutes past

4

21 minutes past

22 minutes past

5

24 minutes past

26 minutes past

27 minutes past

28 minutes past

29 minutes past

Name:

Worksheet: Minutes to the hour

Fill in the missing times.

1 minute to
2 minutes to
3 minutes to
4 minutes to
5 minutes to
6 minutes to
7 minutes to

11

9 minutes to

10

11 minutes to

12 minutes to

9

15 minutes to

17 minutes to

18 minutes to

8

21 minutes to

22 minutes to

7

24 minutes to

26 minutes to
27 minutes to
28 minutes to
29 minutes to

This clock shows 23 minutes to 4.
Look at the hour hand. It is between 3 and 4.
In 23 minutes it will be on the 4 at 4 o'clock.
37 minutes ago it was on the 3 at 3 o'clock.
Here are two ways we can write the time:

23 minutes to 4

or

3.37

Name:

Worksheet: Counting the minutes

Colour the bars on the digital clocks to show the times that are on the analogue clocks.

Name:

Worksheet: Today at school

What have you done at school today?

Write five sentences.
In each sentence, write the time in two ways.
Here is an example of the first two sentences:

I arrived at the playground at about twenty minutes to nine (8.40 a.m.).

The bell went at ten minutes to nine (8.50 a.m.).

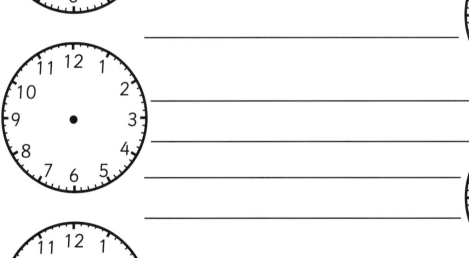

What did you do yesterday afternoon?

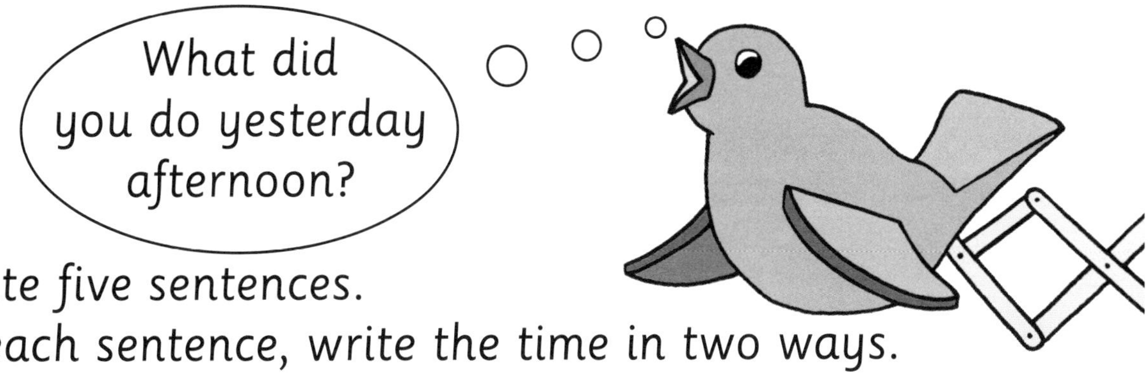

Write five sentences.
In each sentence, write the time in two ways.
Here is an example of the first two sentences:

I left school at half past three (3.30 p.m.).

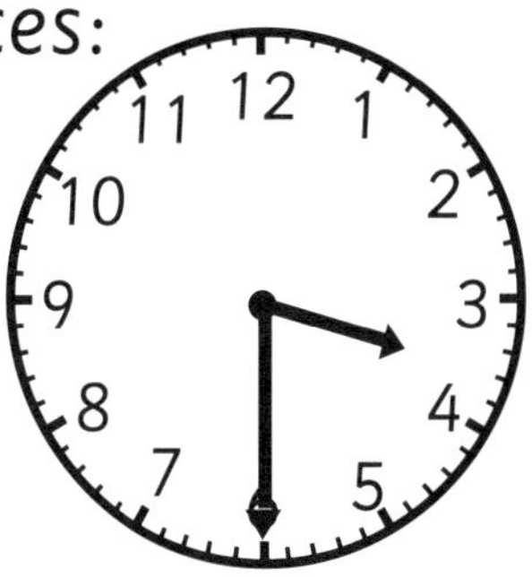

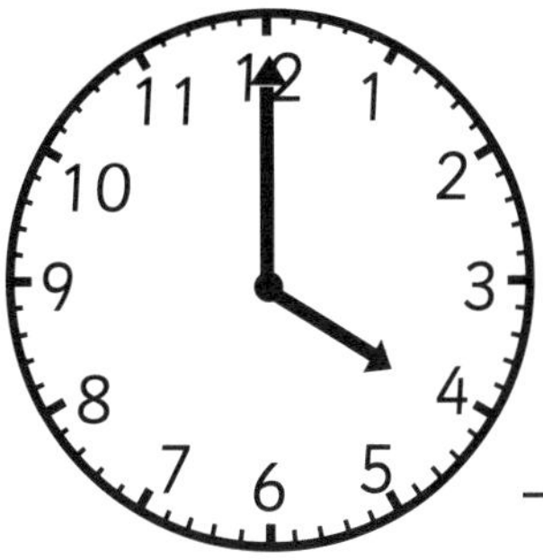

I arrived home at 4 o'clock (4.00 p.m.).

_____

_____

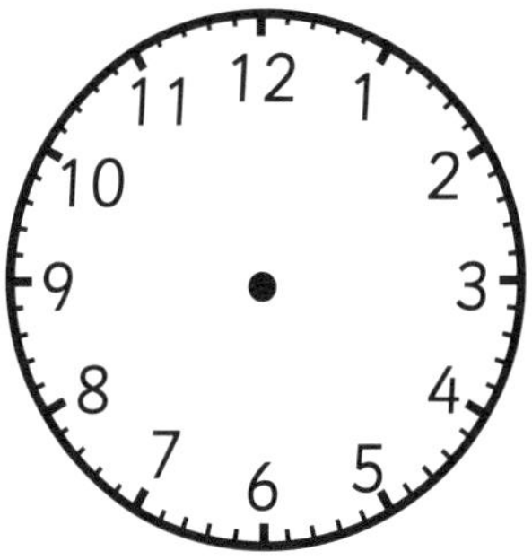

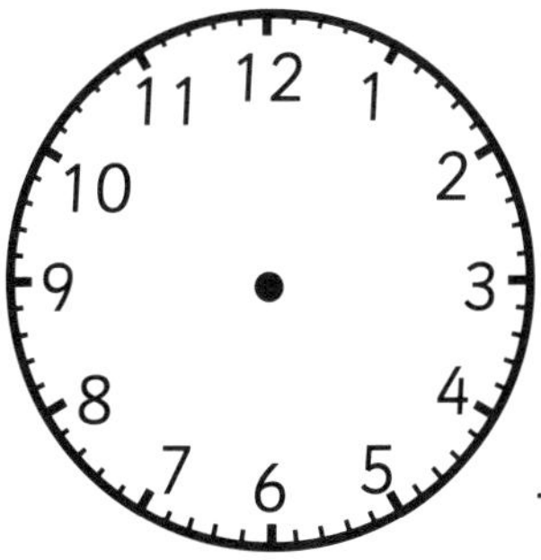

_____

_____

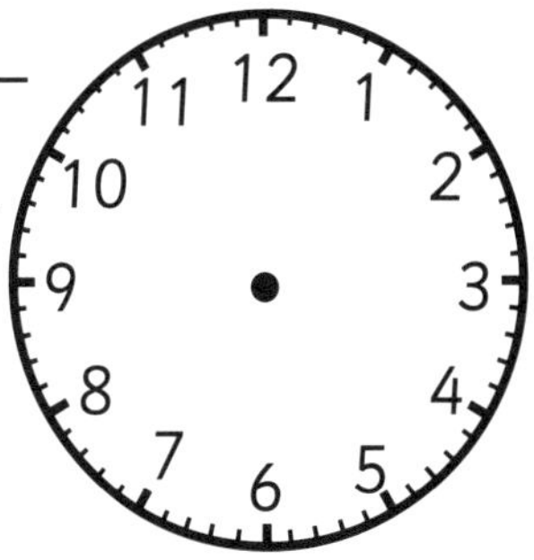

_____

_____

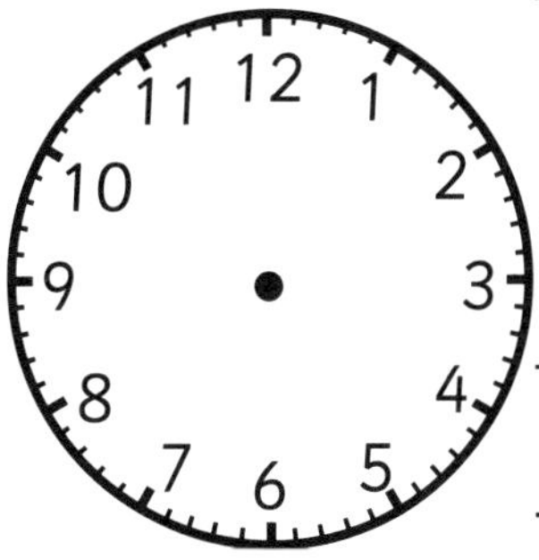

_____

_____

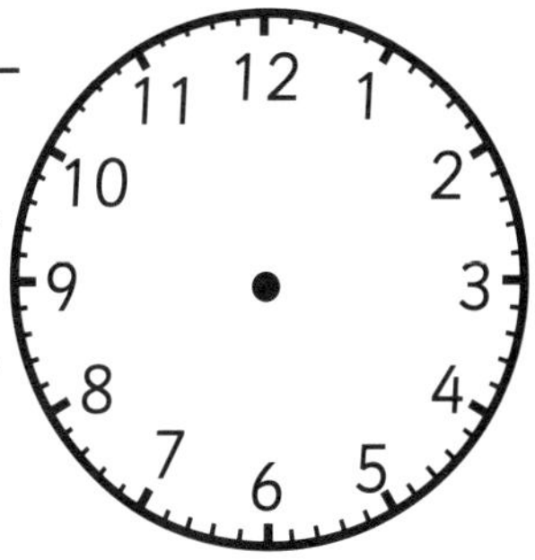

50

Name:

Calendar for 2005

January
M	T	W	T	F	S	S
					1	2
3	4	5	6	7	8	9
10	11	12	13	14	15	16
17	18	19	20	21	22	23
24	25	26	27	28	29	30
31						

February
M	T	W	T	F	S	S
	1	2	3	4	5	6
7	8	9	10	11	12	13
14	15	16	17	18	19	20
21	22	23	24	25	26	27
28						

March
M	T	W	T	F	S	S
	1	2	3	4	5	6
7	8	9	10	11	12	13
14	15	16	17	18	19	20
21	22	23	24	25	26	27
28	29	30	31			

April
M	T	W	T	F	S	S
				1	2	3
4	5	6	7	8	9	10
11	12	13	14	15	16	17
18	19	20	21	22	23	24
25	26	27	28	29	30	

May
M	T	W	T	F	S	S
						1
2	3	4	5	6	7	8
9	10	11	12	13	14	15
16	17	18	19	20	21	22
23	24	25	26	27	28	29
30	31					

June
M	T	W	T	F	S	S
		1	2	3	4	5
6	7	8	9	10	11	12
13	14	15	16	17	18	19
20	21	22	23	24	25	26
27	28	29	30			

July
M	T	W	T	F	S	S
				1	2	3
4	5	6	7	8	9	10
11	12	13	14	15	16	17
18	19	20	21	22	23	24
25	26	27	28	29	30	31

August
M	T	W	T	F	S	S
1	2	3	4	5	6	7
8	9	10	11	12	13	14
15	16	17	18	19	20	21
22	23	24	25	26	27	28
29	30	31				

September
M	T	W	T	F	S	S
			1	2	3	4
5	6	7	8	9	10	11
12	13	14	15	16	17	18
19	20	21	22	23	24	25
26	27	28	29	30		

October
M	T	W	T	F	S	S
					1	2
3	4	5	6	7	8	9
10	11	12	13	14	15	16
17	18	19	20	21	22	23
24	25	26	27	28	29	30
31						

November
M	T	W	T	F	S	S
	1	2	3	4	5	6
7	8	9	10	11	12	13
14	15	16	17	18	19	20
21	22	23	24	25	26	27
28	29	30				

December
M	T	W	T	F	S	S
			1	2	3	4
5	6	7	8	9	10	11
12	13	14	15	16	17	18
19	20	21	22	23	24	25
26	27	28	29	30	31	

Look at the calendar for 2005.

Answer the questions.

Which two months start on a Saturday?

Which three months start on a Tuesday?

Which month starts on a Sunday?

Which month starts on a Wednesday?

Which months start on a Friday?

Which month starts on a Monday?

Which months start on a Thursday?

How many months have 31 days?

How many months have 30 days?

Which month doesn't have either 30 or 31 days?

Use your best handwriting to copy this rhyme.

Thirty days has September,

April, June and November.

All the rest have thirty-one,

Except for February alone,

Which has twenty-eight days clear

And twenty-nine in each leap year.

Which months have thirty-one days?

Which months have thirty days?

How many days does February usually have? ☐

How many days does February have in a leap year?

☐

How many days are there usually in a year? ☐

How many days are there in a leap year? ☐

Look Learn ↓	Fold to cover	Look Learn ↓	Write the month	Write the number of days
January		has 31 days		has ☐ days.
February		has 28 days & 29 in a leap year.		has ☐ days. and ☐ days in a leap year.
March		has 31 days		has ☐ days.
April		has 30 days		has ☐ days.
May		has 31 days		has ☐ days.
June		has 30 days		has ☐ days.
July		has 31 days		has ☐ days.
August		has 31 days		has ☐ days.
September		has 30 days		has ☐ days.
October		has 31 days		has ☐ days.
November		has 30 days		has ☐ days.
December		has 31 days		has ☐ days.

The Earth spins around completely every 24 hours. That's why there's 24 hours in a day.

The earth takes approximately $365\frac{1}{4}$ days to travel around the Sun. That's why most years have 365 days, but every fourth year we have an extra day – this is called a leap year. The year 2000 was a leap year. Write these years in the correct boxes below.

2004	1996	1991	2007	1998
2020	2026	2005	1997	2008
2016	1990	1992	2040	2006
1994	2056	2080	1972	2009

LEAP YEARS	NOT LEAP YEARS
___ ___ ___	___ ___ ___
___ ___	___ ___
___ ___ ___	___ ___ ___
___ ___	___ ___

Midnight is the very end of one day ...

...and it's the very start of a new day.

Most digital clocks look like this at midnight:

Analogue clocks look like this at midnight:

We say that the time is <u>12 midnight</u>.

Here are the clocks at 1 o'clock in the morning ...

The time is 1 a.m.

2 o'clock in the morning ...

The time is 2 a.m.

3 o'clock in the morning ...

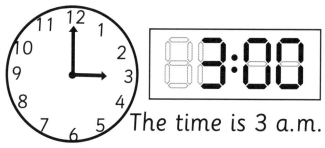

The time is 3 a.m.

Show the times on the clocks.

4 a.m.

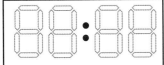

5 a.m.

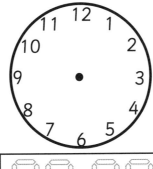
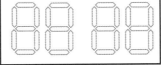

6 a.m.

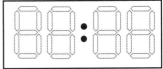

7 a.m.

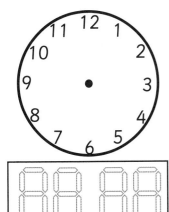

8 a.m.

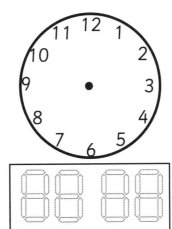

9 a.m.

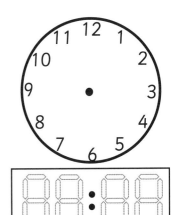

10 a.m.

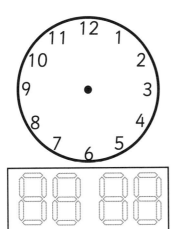

11 a.m.

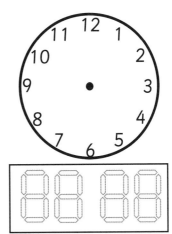

Name:

Worksheet: Afternoon and evening

Digital clocks look like this at noon:

Analogue clocks look like this:

the time is **12 noon**

At 1 o'clock in the afternoon some digital clocks look like this …

… and some look like this.

This digital clock shows **24-hour clock** times.

Complete the missing times on these 24-hour digital clocks. We have done the first three for you.

1 p.m.

2 p.m.

3 p.m.

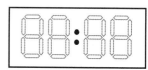

4 p.m.

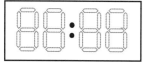

5 p.m.

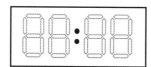

6 p.m.

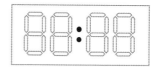

7 p.m.

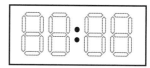

8 p.m.

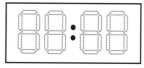

9 p.m.

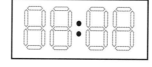

10 p.m.

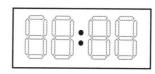

11 p.m.